The Rainbow Picnic

Advance
PUBLISHERS

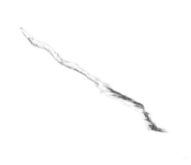

Advance Publishers, L.C.
1060 Maitland Center Commons, Suite 365
Maitland, FL 32751 USA

10 9 8 7 6 5 4 3 2 1
ISBN-10: 1-57973-389-1

Mickey stood at the Clubhouse window. "Gee, I can't believe it's raining again," he said. "I guess we can't have our picnic today."

"Actually, I like it when it rains," said Minnie.

"Why?" asked Mickey. He was surprised.

"My book says that rainbows come after the rain," Minnie explained. "And I love rainbows!"

Read About Rainbows

Minnie wishes she could see a rainbow every day.

RAINBOWS

When the rays of the sun and misty sheets of rain come together in the sky, a rainbow sometimes appears. Have you ever seen a rainbow?

When Donald, Daisy, and Goofy arrived, Minnie showed everyone her rainbow book.

"I like orange the best," said Goofy.

"I like blue," said Daisy.

"I like purple," said Minnie. "And red. And green. Oh! I like them all!"

Then Minnie had an idea. "It's supposed to be sunny tomorrow. We could have our picnic then—and make it a rainbow picnic!"

"What's a rainbow picnic?" asked Donald.

"We all bring foods that are the colors of the rainbow," explained Minnie.

Daisy clapped her hands. "What a great idea!"

Minnie likes all the colors in a rainbow.

RAINBOWS
Colors in a rainbow always appear in the same order: red, orange, yellow, green, blue, indigo, and violet.

Mickey and Minnie love picking and eating red berries.

RASPBERRIES

A fruit is a part of a plant that holds seeds. These raspberries are red and slightly fuzzy.

Mickey and Minnie wanted to find something red for the rainbow picnic.

"These berries will be perfect," said Minnie.

"And delicious!" added Mickey.

Daisy found something else that was red: a watermelon!

"I love watermelon," said Daisy. Then she sliced and diced it up to make a yummy fruit salad.

Watermelon is a sweet addition to a picnic.

WATERMELONS

When you cut into many fruits, such as cucumbers, tomatoes, watermelons, and apples, you can see their tiny seeds!

Although Donald bought his lemons at the store, they originally came from a tree.

LEMONS
These lemons are a fruit that grows on trees.

Donald wanted to bring something yellow to the picnic. He walked to the store to look at all the fruits and vegetables.

"How about lemons? They're yellow," he said to himself. "I'll just take a few of the big ones on the bottom."

Crash! Boing! The lemons came falling down like an avalanche!

"Wak!" Donald cried.

Things for Picnic:
Tablecloth
Napkins
Plates
Fruits

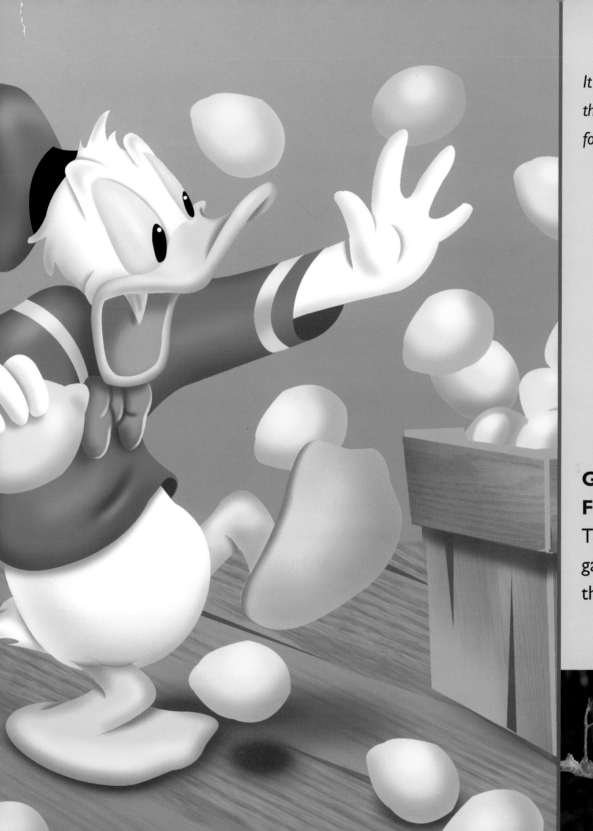

It looks like Donald isn't the only one looking for lemons!

GATHERING FOOD

This dormouse is gathering food for the upcoming winter.

Donald now knows that not all fruit tastes as sour as lemons.

PLUMS

Crispy apples, slurpy watermelons, and plump plums are all fruits.

When Donald returned to the Clubhouse with the lemons, he discovered a problem. Lemons tasted sour! They couldn't eat lemons at the picnic!

"Maybe there's a Mouseketool that could help you figure out what to do with the lemons," suggested Mickey. "Oh, Toodles!"

Toodles arrived with the Mouseketools: a bowl, a pitcher, and the Mystery Mouseketool.

"I could use the pitcher and make lemonade!" Donald exclaimed.

"Right!" said Mickey. "We've got ears! Say cheers!"

So Donald went to the kitchen and made lemonade from the lemons.

Donald makes great lemonade.

LEMONADE

Fruits contain lots of vitamins and minerals. Many drinks are made with fruit, such as lemonade, fruit punch, grape juice, orange juice, and apple juice.

Minnie grows peas in her garden.

VEGETABLES

What are parts of a plant that people eat? Vegetables! These peas come in pods.

In the kitchen, Minnie searched for something green. She found some pickles, but she was sure there must be more green things to bring. She looked through the rest of the kitchen cupboards but couldn't find anything.

"Hmm. Where else can I look?" she said. "Oh! I can look in the vegetable garden." Minnie ran outside and happily found some green vegetables.

"Peas will work," she said. "And I can pick some lettuce and make a tasty salad, too."

Since lettuce is green, it's perfect for the picnic!

LETTUCE

Lettuce is a plant's leaves, celery is a stem, broccoli is a flower, and beets are roots. Lettuce tastes good in salads.

Daisy can't get enough blueberries!

BERRIES
There are five layers in a deciduous forest. The fourth layer is the herb layer, which is made up of plants such as wildflowers and berries.

Daisy knew just what she wanted for something blue: blueberries. But she couldn't hold all the blueberries in her arms. She put them in her purse, but that soon filled up, too. There was only one thing left to do...
"Oh, Toodles!" she called.

Toodles appeared with the remaining Mouseketools: a bowl and the mystery tool.

"A bowl would hold the blueberries," Daisy decided.

She gathered all the berries and put them in the bowl. They fit perfectly!

Berries, berries, everywhere!

BERRIES
Brightly colored berries grow in the tundra in summer.

Goofy can't resist a juicy orange.

ORANGES
Oranges are juicy and sweet.

Meanwhile, Goofy drove to a nearby orange grove.

"A-hyuck! What's more orange than oranges?" he said with a laugh.

Along the way, he spotted some other things that were orange.

"I see one, two, three butterflies!" he said.

He also saw some pretty orange flowers growing on the side of the road. Then he parked the Toon Car and loaded it up with oranges for the picnic.

The best place to get an orange is right off a tree.

ORCHARDS

A lot of the food we eat grows from the land. Farmers grow fruit trees in their orchards and vegetables in their fields.

Daisy wants to bring bunches and bunches of grapes to the picnic since grapes are in season.

SEASONS

In some parts of the world, the weather changes when the seasons change. The types of plants that bloom and the behavior of animals also can change from one season to the next.

Daisy tried to think of something purple she could bring to the picnic. She decided to take a walk.

"Maybe I'll think of something along the way," she thought.

She rounded a corner and gasped. "Oh, my! What lovely purple flowers!"

"Oh, how pretty!"
Daisy says of the
purple flowers.

SEASONS
Brightly colored
flowers blossom in
the spring.

Then she gasped again. "Grapes! I forgot they were in season!"

She grabbed some bunches of grapes—and flowers—and hurried back to the Clubhouse. It was almost picnic time!

Goofy sure hopes that ants are not coming to spoil the picnic!

ANTS

Although they are small, ants are incredibly strong insects. Some ants can carry objects that are twenty times their size!

That afternoon, it was time for the rainbow picnic. All the friends brought their colorful foods to the table in the meadow.

"Oh! Thank you, everyone," Minnie gushed. "This all looks wonderful."

"And colorful!" added Daisy.

"Come on, let's eat!" said a hungry Donald.

Daisy added some yummy yellow pineapple to her fruit salad.

BROMELIADS
You can see bromeliad leaves at your grocery store. Just look at a pineapple. Can you see the thick, green leaves? Pineapples are bromeliads.

It looks like Figaro has a new friend!

MEADOWS

A meadow is land that is wide and open and covered with grass. Many insects, plants, and animals make their homes in the meadow. Mice and bunnies hide in the tall grass. Hummingbirds and butterflies fly happily around the flowers.

"I know they aren't the color of a rainbow, but I just had to bring hot dogs," Mickey said to Minnie. "Besides, what's a picnic without hot dogs?!"

Minnie giggled, then she said, "I think it's a wonderful idea. Oh, Mickey, I'm having such a great time, I want to remember it always."

"Maybe it's time for the Mystery Mouseketool," said Mickey. "Everyone say, 'Oh, Toodles!'"

The Mystery Mouseketool was a camera. Everyone say cheese!

"Super cheers! We've used all our Mouseketools!" said Mickey.

Minnie couldn't resist bringing some colorful flowers to the picnic.

FLOWERS

Flowers are the pretty blossoms on plants. They come in many colors, shapes, and sizes. They grow in the woods, in gardens, in parks, and in yards.

"I just love rainbows!" says Minnie.

DOUBLE RAINBOWS

At times, you can see a double rainbow in the sky—a bright rainbow and a second, lighter-colored rainbow above it. The colors in the lighter rainbow always appear in the opposite order of the bright rainbow!

Just as they were finishing, it began to rain. They ran toward the Clubhouse. Suddenly Minnie stopped. She spotted something in the distance.

"Could it be?" she wondered.

Yes! It was a rainbow just for their rainbow picnic!